advantage

speech therapy services

Praise for ABCs of Speech

Robyn provides practical and easily implementable ways to help families target their child's speech and language goals through everyday activities and routines. As a pediatric Speech-Language Pathologist, I can provide this wealth of ideas to the families I work with, knowing that they will be able to use this book to help their child succeed.

Brook, SLP

As a preschool teacher, I always look for ways to communicate and understand children during their developmental stages. The ABCs book gives us a bridge on which to meet each student and give them the utmost help and education we can give.

Shelby, Preschool teacher

As a former reading specialist and a mom of three girls, I am impressed with how Robyn brings books, games, and everyday life experiences into speech activities She explains educational terminology so that ALL people reading this book can utilize and comprehend the activities presented to enhance their child's speech. Parents, teachers, grandparents, and babysitters will easily be able to implement this book into their daily lives. I wish I had it when my kids were younger.

Meg, Reading Specialist & Mom

As a Pre-k teacher, Robyn's book is a perfect how-to guide to enhance a child's understanding and learning when it comes to speech. I have had multiple students who have needed speech therapy, but what is so great about this book is that I now know different methods that I can incorporate in the classroom as well. This book is straightforward, easy to read, and gives clear direction on different learning techniques. The information in this book will alter my teaching in the classroom for the better. Thank you, Robyn!

Dajah, PreSchool Teacher

As a parent whose child is currently taking speech therapy lessons with Robyn, the book, "ABC's of Speech" provides wonderful and practical exercises that greatly help to positively reinforce the periodic therapy lessons in a fun and engaging way. Throughout the book, I recognized many teachings that Robyn uses when working with my daughter, and I'm easily able to carry forward a number of these teaching concepts at home. Therapy lessons can work wonders for kids, and it's also important to strengthen and compliment these teachings outside of the classroom. The "ABC's of Speech" book is the perfect supplementary communication tool for all ages!

Blake, Dad

OF SPEECH

Tips and Tricks to Help Your Child's Speech Development

Robyn M. Drothler, M.ED CCC-SLP

Published in the United States of America

Wellness Book Endeavors
c/o Authentic Endeavors Publishing
Clarks Summit, PA 18411

Book Interior and E-book Design by Amit Dey
Cover Design and Interior Art by Aljon Inertia

The ABCs of Speech

ISBN: 978-1-955668 56-9 (Paperback)
ISBN: 978-1-955668-57-6 (EBook)
Library of Congress Control Number: 2023907356

Dedication

Dedicated to all the families that have helped my company become what it is today. I am grateful for all the inspiration I have gained through working with my clients who have helped me become a better therapist.

Table of Contents

Foreword

By Evelyn M. Lopez, MS, CCC-SLP

To the kind people who believe in the power of communication:

Robyn and I have been colleagues and dear friends for many years. Her enthusiasm for all things speech therapy is electric and contagious. She is forever thinking about her clients and what she can do to help them become successful communicators. The joy in her conversations intensified when she announced that she was finally making her dream happen to create this book. Robyn is so driven and rarely says no or backs down when faced with a challenge. She has worked tirelessly with children in her community and is in constant motion to do better and be better for them. It is only natural, then, that she would find a way to create a resource to support the little talkers of this world further.

Robyn's creativity is constantly flowing. If one idea doesn't work, she's almost always got a backup. Her wish with this book is to continue creatively supporting children as they develop into effective communicators, even when the speech therapist is not around. While this book is not meant to replace the speech therapist, it can be a very powerful tool to supplement our work.

As therapists, we are always working on helping our clients generalize the skills they learn in therapy. We hope that children can take what they learn in the session and carry over that new skill across all settings. The activities in this clever book help support that. Robyn has carefully curated each activity.

She has poured over 26 years of knowledge and ideas into each page. The best part is that they can be easily tasked to children to increase their opportunities for communication across various settings.

Parents and teachers will find it helpful to use at home and in the classroom. Robyn has ensured that each page also provides support behind her ideas by providing useful, educational information to help parents understand the why behind each one of her activities.

I hope everyone who picks up this book feels the love and positive energy Robyn has poured into it!

Acknowledgments

To my mentors - Burge and Tasha

I am very thankful for your persistence and dedication to helping me achieve not only success in my business with this book but also personal achievements to be the best version of myself to create this resource book for families and educators. I have learned so much from you both and am thankful for the lessons.

To my professor at Wooster - Dr. Rea

Thank you for molding me into the therapist I have become. I am forever grateful for the hands-on experience that the Speech and Hearing clinic on campus at Wooster provided to help prepare me for the real world.

To my professor/advisor at VSU - Dr. Smith

Thank you for your unconditional support in helping me navigate classes and clinic programs at VSU. Your time and wisdom were priceless to me.

About the Author

Robyn Drothler, M.ED CCC-SLP

Robyn Drothler is the owner of Advantage Speech Therapy Services Inc. (ASTS).

She graduated from the College of Wooster (Ohio) in 1995 with an undergraduate degree in Communication Sciences and Disorders and a minor in Psychology.

She worked for three years in the Manatee County School District in Florida. In May 2000, Robyn graduated from Valdosta State University with a Master's in Education.

During three years in Gwinnett County, GA, post-graduate, she earned her Certificate of Clinical Competence while also working for private therapy companies. In 2002, Robyn founded ASTS.

Robyn is a certified member of ASHA, The American Speech-Language-Hearing Association, and state certified in Georgia. She continues expanding and developing her knowledge and skills post-graduate with continuing education courses.

Robyn is experienced in, but not limited to, Articulation/ Phonological disorders, Developmental Delays, Autism/ PDD, and Down Syndrome.

My Philosophy

I believe in having fun with kids and playing while they learn. I make therapy enjoyable so they don't realize they are really "working." At the same time, my sessions are structured and client-focused. Each session is led by the child, using their interests as our guide as we work toward achieving their therapy goals!

It is a delicate balance. If a child wants to share a story or tell me about a new game they have, I'm all about working that narrative into our session. I want to make therapy reflect real life by including their interests, not by simply assigning worksheets or drilling certain speech sounds. Building skills, using topics they are interested in, helps them adjust to real life more effectively.

This book will show you how to engage with children and teach them skills without them even realizing they are "working." Each page reveals educational skills to address in a fun way. You will also find informative content on how to interpret daily interactions with children. Using each letter of the alphabet, I provide specific ideas that you will find helpful as you engage with them. I will show you how to use everyday activities to encourage communication.

I've been working in the field long enough to know that I feel much more effective as a therapist working privately, one on one, with kids compared to the school system. Not only do I see more progress in achievement towards goals, but the parents are also more involved and there is more carryover of skills as a result. This book is an extension of the work I've shared with parents, guardians, teachers and other healthcare professionals involved in the therapy process.

Robyn Drothler
(404) 784-1252 mobile
678-624-9599 fax
robyn@advantagespeech.com
www.advantagespeech.com

Introduction

Effective and proper speech is something many of us take for granted. Speech development is critical for effective communication, but the process of helping your child speak may feel overwhelming and frustrating.

Over the years, families have asked me for carryover ideas and suggestions on what to do with their children between therapy appointments. As a result, the resource book of tips and tricks you are holding was born.

My mission is to provide a warm and loving environment where children love to play and play to learn and where parents and caregivers learn strategies to carryover skills and enhance therapeutic progress.

This book is intended for parents, family members, teachers, mentors, and other specialists working with those struggling or learning to communicate. It provides creative ideas, such as using toys and games, to incorporate speech and language goals into everyday activities. The ideas will encourage more communication by transforming receptive tasks into expressive ones.

Robyn Drothler, M.ED CCC-SLP

ABCs of Speech

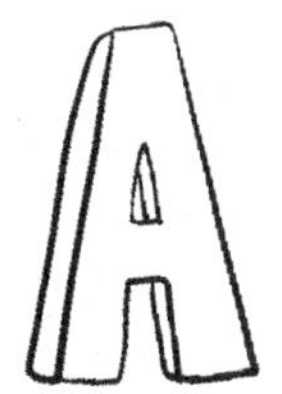

ARTICULATION

Developmental milestones indicate that kids should babble by six to eight months and use one to two words by 12 months. Early sounds produced include (but are not limited to) /m/, /b/, /p/, and /d/. All sounds are not learned or developed until around age eight. Therefore, certain errors and difficult sounds are expected and can typically develop over time.

Children are taught how to communicate. Therefore, if you give a child something for "free" (i.e., not requiring them to say or do something to get it), they will ultimately just point/grunt/push/pull to get what they want. It is imperative that you teach them to use their words so that later on, they will not become confused and ultimately frustrated during this process, sometimes leading to tantrums.

ACTION & REACTION

Teach children that an **ACTION causes a REACTION.** For example, kids need to do or say something to get something. More specifically, encourage children to say or do something to get what they want. Knowing what they want is half the battle. Show them an object and

teach them to say it. If you don't know what they are trying to express, have them "show" you. Once you see the item, you can say, "Oh, you want a cookie? Tell me, 'cookie.'" Encourage them to repeat the word so that *next time* they will know what to say to get it. If they cannot do it independently, model sounds, syllables, or words for them to imitate.

ALPHABET

While talking about sounds, you can also practice the alphabet using word association. "A is for Apple … a, a, a ('æ'). B is for baby, buh buh buh. C is for cat, kuh kuh kuh," etc. For sounds such as /b/, /p/, /f/, /v/, /w/, and /m/, point to your lips because that is where these sounds are formed. However, for the sounds /k/ and /g/, you should point to your throat/neck region; those sounds are formed in a different area. On the other hand, /s/, /z/, /t/, /d/, /n/, and /l/ are somewhat visible and can be taught by using a mirror so your child can SEE where they are putting their tongue. Adding something like peanut butter or pudding where they need to put their tongue can help with placement.

Another tongue-positioning technique is to use a tongue depressor or a popsicle stick to help your child position their tongue in the right articulatory spot so they can FEEL the position. Adding something yummy on the end and placing it on the spot where the sound needs to be produced adds a fun element and requires them to find the food, which teaches them where their tongue needs to be. Have them say the sound when they find the food so they don't lose the spot when the food goes away without having tried to say the sound.

ACTIONS

Actions are crucial to help kids understand what people *do*. It also helps to address people using proper nouns and pronouns, which can take time to learn. He is, she is, they are, etc., can provide a leading phrase to help your child fill in the blank. Eventually, they will be able to name the picture/action, etc., on their own without your cue.

I want
more puzzles.

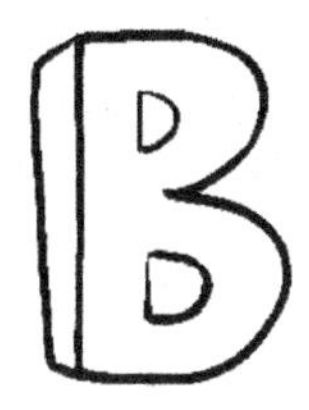

BE PRESENT

Take the time to make the most of everyday situations to help your child meet their speech goals. By making it part of your day, *every day*, it will eventually become natural.

BEHAVIOR

Behavior is communication, and it is how children express themselves. When your child misbehaves, they are likely frustrated. It is helpful to assist the situation with signs and other forms of communication to reduce the behaviors. The goal is to understand what they are trying to express and help them elicit a more appropriate way to engage. Once you give them a better system which can include PECS (*Picture Exchange Communications System,)* a few signs, or teach a few sounds to promote verbalizations to "get" something, they will be more successful and ready to learn and verbally express their wants and needs. Signing *does* encourage communication - it *does not* hinder it.

Additionally, just because your child isn't "talking" doesn't mean your child isn't communicating with you. Pay attention, and you'll recognize what is being "said" non-verbally through body language, facial expressions, or just by pointing and gesturing. Pairing meaning with those expressions is a more functional way to interact and engage with your child.

BODY PARTS

Use a variety of strategies to teach body parts. You can use games like Mr. Potato Head or sing songs that help your child speak the different body parts—like the song *Head & Shoulders, Knees, and Toes*. If your child gets frustrated, slow down. If you are singing a song, stop the music so *they* can say the word, or if you need to help them say the words correctly.

BOOKS

While reading books, have your child think about what might happen next. You can discuss the book's sequence. *What happened first?* and *What happened last? Who is the story about?* and *Where did they go?* They can draw pictures of three to four parts of the story and put them in order. There are sequencing games and iPad apps to help kids learn to put things in order.

Children hear repetitive verses, which eventually get embedded in their heads. After reading certain books multiple times, start leaving out words to get them to fill in the blank. Use gestures to help promote word recall, such as pointing to your eyes for "see" or your ears for "hear." Good examples are: *Brown Bear, Brown Bear, What Do You See?* or *Polar Bear, Polar Bear, What Do You Hear?* Dr. Seuss' books are also helpful since the illustrations provide meaningful clues.

Good Night Moon is an excellent book to help build a vocabulary of objects they would see in their room/house. Allow your child to point to the objects as you read the words. Eventually, your child can "read" it themselves by pointing to various other objects not necessarily named in the book on their own due to the repetitive nature of the book.

My First Word Book is an excellent book to help with vocabulary development. There are so many things you can teach by branching off of this book. The pictures are already categorized into body parts, the beach, farm animals, zoo animals, food, shapes, colors, etc. Look at various pictures, talk about a specific picture and then ask questions about them. For example, we have a clock at our house that tells us the time. *What do we do with a clock?* Here are some shoes. We need to wear shoes on our feet so our feet don't hurt when we walk. *Why do we wear shoes?* I see a jacket that keeps us warm in the winter. *When do we wear a jacket?*

The *Carl* book series is an excellent choice of wordless books. They require the reader to make up and tell the story in their own words. They typically have a few words at the beginning and end, but each *Carl* book allows you to look at the pictures and create a new version each time you read it. This is an excellent opportunity for kids to tell a story when they have yet to learn to read. Not only does it help them put words together to form a sentence, but it can also help them practice *new vocabulary* and *speech sounds* as well. Start with a picture walk by just flipping through the pages slowly in order to see what the story is about. Based on your child's age, you may have to provide the first storytelling experience to show them how to do it. If they copy your story the first time through, don't worry, because eventually, they will be able to do it on their own in their own way. Initially, they are just learning the process.

Do not feel obligated to use the written text each time when using books. Ask several questions such as, *What is the monkey holding in his hands? Where do you think they are going? What do you think will happen next?* You can turn the page and see if they got it right. If they can't come up with a guess on their own, you can turn the page to prompt your child to formulate their thoughts. Use the page as a clue. *Predictions* also help you incorporate grammar. For example, she is drinking milk, and then she drank the milk. Or she is climbing the tree to get the cat...and then she climbed the tree, got the cat, and brought it down safely.

To help with **READING COMPREHENSION**, buy a beach ball and write questions about the book on each color of the ball. For example, *What is the title? Who is the author? Who are the main characters? What is the setting? What happened in the story? How did it end? What was your favorite part?* By asking these types of questions in a fun-filled way, children look forward to discussing the events in the book. Then, you can toss the ball back and forth with your child and answer the question your hand lands on.

CALENDAR

Visually explain what a week, month, and year look like. *How many days are in a week, month, and year? What comes before Monday? What day do we go to church? When do you have baseball practice?* Include holidays in the discussion. *When are certain holidays, such as Halloween?* Incorporate the concept of time into learning about the calendar. For example, a day has 24 hours, one hour has 60 minutes, and one minute has 60 seconds. Which is longer, one minute or 65 seconds? How long is our vacation? If we leave on Saturday and return on Tuesday, how many days will we be gone?

You can also create word problems using a calendar. Show how to count weeks using seven-day increments, Monday to Monday or Thursday to Thursday; that is automatically seven days. Discuss the concept of a month by asking, *How many **months** are in a **year**? How many **days** are in a **year?** and How many **days** are in a **month?*** Some months have more days than others, and every month has a different holiday. You can expand this lesson each month by talking about the upcoming holiday and what it means/represents to your family.

CARRYOVER

Carryover is key for home reinforcement. There should be continuity between therapy sessions and the child's home environment. It is unrealistic to expect your child to reach their goals by *only* meeting with a therapist twice weekly for 30 minutes. Parents need to reinforce what is worked on in the sessions by doing those things at home with their child.

CATALOGS

Using catalog images for furniture or clothes, you can have your child cut out the picture and write their own description (adjectives) for that item. This promotes a discussion of fabrics, sizes, gender differences, etc. If you don't have catalogs, you can use pantry items or things in their closet as examples.

CATEGORIZE

You can group things, such as pictures of food or objects from any game, puzzle, or picture book. Categorize them by color, shape, size, animal features, household items, food, etc. Talk about how they are the *same* and how they are *different*. How could they group a few items together? They can then remove some items or add new items to make another connection between the pictures or objects (i.e., shift items between categories.) For example, a sun can be something *hot*, but it can also be something *in the sky*. A car can be something *with wheels*, but it can also be a *vehicle*).

CAUSE AND EFFECT

To practice cause and effect, use toys that require *action*. Think of toys where you have to **do** something for something to **happen**. For example, when you hit the ball on the top of the toy, it goes down the chute -or- when you push a button, a light comes on. Kids will learn early on that **an action causes a reaction.**

CHOICES

Give your child choices so they can choose the one they want while using their words. Don't accept "that one" or "this one." Be sure to label the pictures and elaborate on what the child says. For example, if they label an object as a spoon, say, "Yes, that's a spoon. We need it to scoop food."

CLUES

When your child doesn't know the answer to something, rather than give it to them upfront, give clues, ask questions, and work on guiding them to the answer. For example: If they want the remote control to change channels, ask, *What do we use to turn the tv on? It has buttons! It'll help you change the channels too!* -or- *Do you need something to scoop your food? It's a utensil, and we keep it in the drawer.* -or- If they need their shoes to go outside, say, *What are you forgetting to put on your feet? I think you'll find them in your closet upstairs!*

COMMITMENT

Your commitment to working on goals and incorporating your child's goals from therapy into your everyday activities is vital for success. *Narrate* what you are doing throughout your day to help your child learn and develop language. Apply a goal while you are doing something fun, so they learn that talking and learning is not all about structured practice. Commit to doing this daily.

CONNECT

When your child is talking and saying words that you clearly notice are in error, but you know what they are saying - recognize that and *connect* with your child. Let them know you understand, but you want to practice saying it more clearly. You can say, "Great job asking for the spoon, but I didn't hear that /s/ sound at the beginning. Can you try it again? Watch me ... /sssssss...puh...ooooo...nuh/." Using a visual model and stretching out the sounds within the word may increase your child's word accuracy.

CONSISTENCY

Consistency is **KEY** to your child's success. Make sure everyone is on board with what you want to do to reach goals with your child. Build consistency with everyone they are exposed to. This includes the babysitter, neighbors, grandparents, friends, siblings, etc. No one should hand anything over to a child without encouraging verbal communication. *Both* parents have to require the same standards for success to be achieved equally. One parent cannot "require" communication while the other parent is passive. *That is counterproductive.*

COUNT

If you have something that needs to be counted, ask your child to help you. You can do this with money, game pieces, socks/laundry items, utensils for setting the table, etc. Use everyday encounters to practice. This activity can also address articulation while saying the numbers!! It is not *just about* counting. It's also following directions, listening, labeling, taking turns (if someone else is with them), grouping/sorting, etc.

CUES

Giving your child words to express themselves isn't cheating when they don't know "what" to say. You can cue them by using words *before* ***they*** start talking. For example, "I want..." and see if they finish or complete the sentence. Encourage them to start with "I want" before getting what they are asking for. Sometimes you may need to say one word at a time to say "I" (I) "want," (want) "a drink," (a drink) "please," (please). Sometimes you may not know what they want, which leads back to offering choices to figure it out. Eventually, slowly pull back your cues to see how they are able to do it on their own.

CURRENCY

We all have currency, which makes us more likely to do something, because we receive something for doing it. Use your child's currency to your benefit. Prompt them with, "Do you want to (choose one: play on your iPad, watch TV, have dessert)? If they say yes (which they most likely will do), say, "FIRST you need to do ___, THEN you get ____." *Motivation* will encourage *action.* Without motivation, they won't work as hard. Technology and toys should not be given automatically. They should be earned.

Ball.
Ball please.

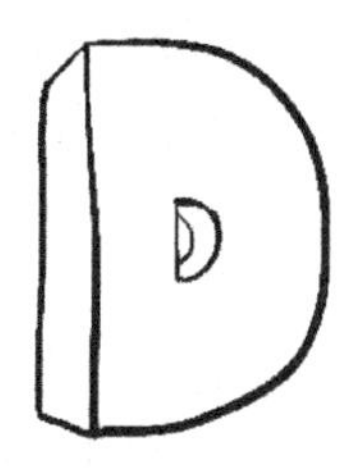

DESCRIBE OR USE DESCRIPTIONS

Think of ways you can describe objects. While driving, you can describe a sign as *big, red, bright*, etc. You might see an old green car that is long, short, big, small, etc.

See how many objects your child can name and have them describe them in as much detail as possible. Example: I see a truck. It is big, long, loud, has many wheels, and is blue! It has a picture of a ___ on it!

Based on your child's age, you may ask them to *describe how they do an activity. How do you tie your shoes? How do you make a sandwich? How do you make an ice cream sundae?* You may actually do these activities with your kids and talk about the process as you are doing it. You can ask them what ingredients are used or what sequence is required to accomplish the task.

When in the grocery store, describe what the items look, feel, or taste like and discuss the different parts of the object. For example, bananas and corn are similar because they are both yellow. However, a banana is a fruit, and corn is a vegetable. Compare foods in other ways. A banana can be peeled, is soft, and easy to chew. A strawberry is not only soft but has a stem, seeds, and is red.

DETAILS

Don't allow your child to say "right there" or "this one" when more specific details are appropriate. Sometimes you need to play "dumb"

to get more communication from your child. Example: What do you mean when you say, "Get it right there?" Where is "right there?" (Even though you know what they are talking about.) The purpose is to get your child to come up with the words to express themselves more clearly.

DEVELOPMENTALLY DELAYED

It can't hurt to get your child tested if you feel that your child isn't functioning similarly to other children in their playgroup or if you instinctively suspect that something just isn't "right." *Early intervention* is critical to getting back on track. If it's a developmental delay, speech therapy can help your child learn the skills they need to build their vocabulary, learn more sounds, and express themselves effectively. Sometimes children understand what they hear (receptive language) but cannot articulate the words they instinctively understand (expressive language).

DIRECTIONS

Verbally share step-by-step directions with your child. For example, explain how to complete the task as you put a DVD in the DVD player or turn on the TV. Following directions is another area that children need to focus on. Start with basic one-step directions and build to more complicated or multi-step ones.

For example, pick up the red car, put the block on the box, or find the teddy bear. You can also create silly commands, such as, "Clap your hands ten times" (one step), "Go to the door and turn around" (two steps), "Say your name, count to 10, and say your ABCs." (three steps). If your child is younger and can't write, have them draw the steps to complete an activity.

I need a paint brush.

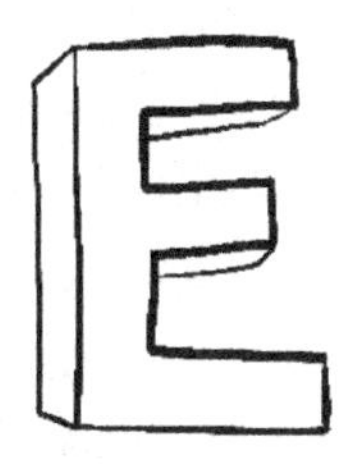

ECHOLALIA

Echolalia is when your child repeats everything you say. They are essentially doing this because *they do not understand what is being asked of them to respond.* Therefore, interject before they respond to your questions (so they don't repeat the question) by providing them with a leading phrase to show them how to react. In other words, immediately following your question, provide a leading phrase to start their answer. For example, you can ask, "Do you want to eat a cookie?" Right away, say, "I want to eat a …" Then, trail off so they can finish the sentence. When finished, have them repeat it if they are able to say the whole thing themselves.

Echolalia is a child's way of trying to respond but not knowing how. Kids will answer questions when they understand what is being asked of them and will echo when they don't.

EYE CONTACT

Encourage **eye contact w**hen communicating, which will enhance conversations. In addition, it will help them know "how" to say the sounds they might be struggling with by seeing the visual model. Use a mirror to help with practice and reinforcement.

EVERYDAY TEACHABLE MOMENTS

Every day is full of teachable moments with opportunities to teach lessons and incorporate vocabulary. These opportunities can be at the

grocery store, during bath time, or when you and your child eat. Meal time is one of the best moments to have generalized conversations, such as using the word "more". If your child is delayed, telling them *what* to say isn't cheating. They just don't know what to say and may need some help. Eventually, they will carry over what they have learned through modeling and cueing as they discover opportunities independently.

ENGAGE AND ELICIT

When your child is doing a particular activity, such as playing, engage in a dialogue about what they are doing. If your child is able to verbalize, ask open-ended questions, not just yes or no questions. Offer choices to help elicit conversation or provide leading phrases.

EXPAND

If your child answers you with a simple answer, you can say, "That is right. I understand, but let's add MORE words." For example, if you ask, "Where do you want to go today?" and they say, "the pool," you could elaborate and have them say, "I want to go to the pool today." If your child is learning to expand their single-word vocabulary, teach them descriptive words to add to the single words they already know. For example, if their vocabulary consists of car, phone, mommy/daddy, up, go, mine, doggie, etc., start pairing these words with new words such as *big* dog, *happy* mommy, *mommy* go, *red* car, phone *ring*, *daddy* phone, *my* doggie, daddy *up*, etc.

What's that?
Can you say
D... Duck?

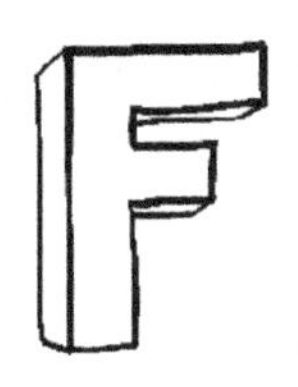

FIRST______ THEN______

When your child has difficulty transitioning, use a visual that reflects the concept of "First____ Then____." This can help them understand what they need to do before they get what they want or need. For example, if your child is getting upset with a given activity, *YOU*, as the adult, determine when you are done; *the child does not.* For example, if they want to get down, but you are not quite done working with them, tell them, "Let's do three more pages, then you can be done." They need to finish talking, and then they can be done. This clearly states what they have to do to get what they want. They can't just shut down to get what they want. If you don't talk it through first, you are teaching them that they get what they want by fussing or having a tantrum. The same goes for any misbehavior, such as crying. If they are crying because they want something, do not give it to them at that moment. Tell them that **FIRST**, they need to stop crying. **THEN**, they can consider *earning* what they are *yearning* for.

FREE

Nothing comes for free. Play dumb. Don't just give your child what they want because you know what it is. Encourage them to *say it.* Encourage them to sign or model sounds if they aren't speaking to "say" something to get something. You can offer choices, but they need to speak. For example, use hand-over-hand to sign "more" or model it for them to repeat it to get "more" of what they want. Keep modeling it for them when they want more of something. Teach them manners. If they talk, encourage saying "I want ___" to get the item in question.

You can also teach the "please" sign. Take your open hand and place it on your chest. Move your hand in a clockwise circle. "I want ___" becomes, "I want ___, please." If, after you try these approaches and they still do not attempt to communicate in whatever capacity works for them, walk away. They will try again if it's important enough for them to want it. Most likely, you are using different rules by following this strategy (i.e., changing the rules on them), so anticipate a tantrum because 'now' you *require* more of your child, which is different for them.

FRIENDS AND FAMILY

The more people are on board with your child's therapy, the better. Consistency is key! Siblings can be a big help in therapy. When they learn that speaking and doing things for their brother or sister isn't helpful, you will have successfully added another member to your team to help them.

FUN

Apply a goal while you are doing something fun, so they understand that talking and learning are not all about structured practice. *It is essential to make learning fun.* As a result, they are more apt to engage with you and less likely to resist. When learning is fun and interesting, children are often unaware they are working on their goals. Do not give up because something is challenging. This is true when you must follow through so they learn they cannot cry to avoid talking or working. However, know your child's limits so that you do not push them into a tantrum due to frustration. Know when to step back and when to push through a tough situation. When you know they need a break, set the criteria, "Let's do three more; then you can be done."

FUNCTIONS

Talk about how an object is used. When using objects, pictures, or occupations, talk about what they do or what purpose the object or person serves. Incorporating occupations can be a creative way to expand beyond a picture. *What does a policeman do? Why does he do that? Where does he work? How does he help people? What does a barber do? What does a teacher do? What do they teach their students? Where do you go to learn?*

Additional examples of questions to ask about functions include:

- *What do you do with your eyes?*
- *What do you do with your shoes?*
- *What do you do with a fork?*
- *What do you do with a car?*
- *What do you do with a drum?*
- *What do you do with a TV?*
- *What does a fish do?*
- *What do you do with a telephone?*

What do you want to do?
Want game.

GAME NIGHT

UNO is a game that encourages matching colors and/or numbers and following specific rules when you get a certain type of card (reverse, skip, draw 2, draw 4, wild, etc.). *Connect 4* requires strategy and problem-solving to prevent your opponent from connecting four pegs in a row in any direction. To add a level of carryover to this game, ask your child to answer a question or practice saying a sound before they take a turn. *Go Fish* encourages questions and vocabulary development, as well as sound reinforcement. Finally, *Pictionary* or *charades* requires participants to think and explain through drawing or acting.

If you see a game in a store and think it might be too complicated for your child, think about how you can *alter* it to make it functional for the time being, knowing that your child will be able to grow with it. Initially, your child may not be able to follow the rules of a game as dictated in the box, but the pictures and new vocabulary exposure may be irreplaceable.

Bottom Line: You do not need to follow the exact directions while playing a game. Instead, adapt and adjust to your child's needs. Allow your child to grow into the game.

Games with hidden motives are always a bonus! It's like at soccer practice when your coach tells you you are going to play *Capture the Flag or Snake*—games that require lots of running!! When preoccupied with playing a fun game, you don't realize the coach is incorporating endurance training into practice. Pretty sneaky! Always consider asking questions or including your child in a task or activity to promote language learning. I always find it funny when 10 minutes into therapy, the child asks me, "When are we going to start," and we have already been working (aka "talking"), yet they had no idea!

Play a game like WIZ KIDS from Discovery Toys where you think of a place (garage, grocery store, ballpark, movie theater) and then think of five letters. Give each letter a point value and see how many words they can develop related to that targeted topic. For example, ask your child to name everything in a bathroom, starting with the letter T (toilet, toothbrush, towel, toenail clippers, and tissues). If you give the letter T two points, they earn two points for every T word they come up with!

GROCERY STORE GAMES

When you go to the grocery store, ask your child questions such as, *Where do you find breakfast foods?* When you find the cereal aisle, then ask, *What else do we need to make our breakfast complete?* Or ask them what they want for dinner. Based on your child's age, you may ask them to tell you how to find that item. In other words, they could give you directions around the store. If you have the app for the store, they can look up items and then direct you on how to get there using the information for that item. Plan ahead and create a fun scavenger hunt for the child to follow while you are shopping.

If your child is old enough, have them write the grocery list, in advance of going to the store. Or, if *you* write it, have them group items together that can be found together in the store (dairy products, cleaning supplies, fruits, vegetables, etc.).

GRAMMAR

For older students: Using a sheet of lined paper, fold the page numerous times vertically to make columns. At the top of each column, write the following (in this order): noun, adjective, verb, pronoun, and adverb. First, ask them to write down at least 20 nouns (person, place, or thing). Next, ask them to describe the nouns by writing words in the adjective column. An *adjective* is a word describing a person, place, or thing. Then think of an *action* that the noun does. This goes in the verb (action) column. Explain that a *pronoun* is a word that can replace a noun and have them list all the different pronouns. The noun column will dictate what pronoun applies, such as he, she, they, or it. Lastly, when finding *adverbs*, have them think of how the noun completed the action. For example, Mom (noun), pretty (adjective), danced (verb), she (pronoun), and happily (adverb). Ultimately you can combine these words to make a sentence. For example, *My pretty mother happily danced the night away to her favorite music.*

GREETINGS

Take opportunities to teach your child how to greet someone. For example, have them say *hi* or *bye* when answering the door or when they are outside the home and see someone they know. It can also include the mail carrier, a food server at a restaurant, or a delivery person! Model what they need to say and have them repeat it.

GEMS

Find out your child's currency and use it to your benefit. If it's for behavior, motivation, or reward— incorporate it! They may love high-fives, M&Ms, stickers, or just spending time with you. Once they complete the request, they earn a reward. Initially, you may need to use a 1:1 ratio of work to reward, then slowly pull that back. They either earn it or they don't. It is imperative to stick to whatever criteria you have set.

GESTURES

Do NOT rely on gestures (pointing, pushing/pulling) for a child to communicate. Knowing what your child wants is the most challenging part. Make them say, approximate, or sign it if they have to, but pointing and grunting are not ok. If you allow them to get what they want by pointing and pulling you to the item, then THAT is what they will do in the future to get what they want because that was the "condition" you gave it to them under.

SCHOOL BUS
Hi, how are you?
Hi!

HELP

Allow others to help. Don't burden yourself. Mother's Morning Out (MMO) programs or playgroups are functional and useful. They not only can take the burden off you, but it is also beneficial for your child to play and learn to communicate with other children. It can also allow you to connect with other parents in similar situations, where you can learn from each other.

HIGH-FIVES

Positively reward your child's successes by giving high-fives or applauding them. Even if your child is not 100% "there" yet, they still deserve recognition. We are shaping the child's behavior, so even if it's not perfect, it's still a GOOD job based on the effort. Regardless, tell them they did an awesome job.

Great job
using your words!

I SPY

You can play the *I Spy* game while you are in the store, the house, or even in the car on a road trip. Give clues to describe what you are "spying." For example, say, "I spy something in the car that starts with the letter /s/ and it's round (steering wheel), or I spy something in the car that moves up and down and is a square (window). Have participants in the game ask yes or no questions. This works on asking questions as well as answering questions for all involved. When you play this game in the grocery store, say, "I'm thinking of something that we need in the produce section. It's yellow, and a monkey likes to eat it. What is it?" (Banana).

IMITATION

Many children learn by imitating others. Do not accept the wrong pronunciation of a word. Instead, offer the corrected version so they know how to speak correctly. It's ok that your child may be unable to say it right, but the important part here is that **YOU** are saying it right. For example: do not say "baba" for a bottle or "wawa" for water. Say the full words "bottle" and "water," so they hear what it is *supposed to be* called.

INTERESTS

Find something your child is interested in and ask them to write about it. For example, if they like a video game, have them write down the steps and directions to teach you how to play. If you find something they enjoy doing, then the work you ask them to do won't necessarily seem as bad. It could be something you can explore together.

INCLUDE

Include your child even when it may take longer and require you to slow down. Working with your child on everyday tasks will pay off in the long run. Don't take the easy way out and do it *for* them. That is not helping them learn. A perfect example would be your child helping you create a grocery list.

INTENT

Make sure when your child is learning to use their words that you don't let them have whatever they want without some sort of communicative intent. A perfect example would be helping to create a grocery list. Even if it's the first sound, like /m/ for milk, or the ASL sign for "more," *require them* to do it. If you say that they need to say a sound or approximate a word to get something, **FOLLOW THROUGH WITH IT**. If you don't, they learn early on that when you say something, you don't mean what you say. They may eventually catch on that if they wait long enough, they can get *out* of doing it. If they try, but don't get it totally right, they have at least tried and attempted to communicate, which counts for something! Be prepared to wait them out, but be patient!

iPad

When playing games on the iPad that are more receptive based, for example, you can pull the iPad away (momentarily) to get your child to say a word, repeat a word, or ask for something. You want them to learn to label, not just understand. This is the difference between *receptive* and *expressive* games. In order to address this, sit next to them and play.

Note:

Receptive language is the understanding of and response to verbal and nonverbal communication from others.

Expressive language is the ability to express wants, needs, thoughts, and feelings verbally and non-verbally.

What do we need from the grocery store?
MILK

JOINT ATTENTION

Joint attention is shifting from "what" they are playing with to "who" they are playing with. This is key in developing language and communication skills. We want to see joint attention during play activities.

JOKING

Have a sense of humor. Learning to speak is frustrating for a child on many levels. So, be silly and work on correcting them in a positive tone. Also, letting them know when *we*, as adults, make mistakes is useful as well. It's human nature as everyone gets tripped up on their words at some point.

Oops...
did I say that?

KEY

The key to progress and reaching goals is *consistency!* Put the effort in, and as the saying goes, you *reap what you sow!* The benefits are priceless when you invest time in your child's learning.

KID-GENERATED IDEAS

Sometimes, a child will think they are in charge and can decide what they are doing in therapy. Little do they know, as therapists, we have our own agenda! However, allowing the child to "choose" helps keep their interest. For example, they may pick the game they want to play given the choices provided to them—all of which meet the goal of what is being worked on with them. They are more inclined to participate and engage when they are interested, so why not let them think *they* are the ones choosing the activity for the day?

KITCHEN

If you are cooking in the kitchen and can use extra hands, allow your child to help with measuring, following directions, reading the recipe, and sequencing the steps. Have them draw a picture when they are done or recite the steps they took to make the dish you just completed.

JANUARY
FEBRUARY
MARCH

LEAD

I often let the child THINK they are taking the LEAD, but I am actually steering them with choices. However, other times, I will "follow" the *child's* lead and incorporate learning opportunities such as vocabulary, imitation, and requesting during their selected activities.

Handwritten LETTERS

If your child is old enough, have them compose a letter to a family member. If they cannot write, have them dictate it to you or include a picture of something they have been doing. Talk about the picture before it is mailed. Write their words at the bottom. If they can write the letter themselves, talk about the different parts of the letter and why that information is necessary. Do this not only for the letter, but also for the envelope. Explain to them *the date, the greeting, the body,* and *the closing of a letter.* Then have them address it and place a stamp on the envelope. Ask questions such as, *Why do we need to put a stamp on the envelope? What would happen if we didn't put a stamp on it? What would happen if we didn't use the correct address for the person we were mailing a letter to? How can we figure out the correct zip code?* Talk about the parts of the address label and why that information is essential (name, street, house #, apartment #, city, state, zip code).

LISTEN

Be a good listener. Listen to your child talk and praise them for making an effort. However, still correct them when necessary. Do not accept "wrong" answers or the wrong pronunciation of a word. They learn and repeat what they are taught. They won't learn to say something "the right way" unless you correct it. There is a fine line between correcting them *all the time* and correcting them *as you see fit*. Make sure you have a balance, as you do not want to over-correct them to the point that they feel like they can't do anything right.

LIBRARY

Go to the library. Even if you don't take out any books, you can at least participate in a story-time class or an arts and crafts event incorporating a lot of language and social interaction with other children. Sometimes the most obvious things to do aren't always that easy to see!

LISTS

Before heading to the grocery store, have your child organize your list into groups. For example, grouping the items in the following areas (produce, cereal, frozen foods, meats, etc.) will help you be organized when moving up and down the aisles. Or, better yet, have them write the list themselves, sounding out the words on their own.

Other suggested lists could include the following:
*things to do over the weekend
*school backpack
*packing list for a trip— suitcase, car ride, or airplane
*things needed at the beach
*sleepover bag
*lunch bag
*picnic

CHILDREN'S SECTION

Good Night Moon
Brown Bear Brown Bear

MAGAZINES AND CATALOGS

Cut pictures of objects or people from magazines to help teach a particular sound. For example, cut out a clock and put a /c/ and /k/ next to it because it starts with the hard /k/ sound but is spelled with a /c/. You can create an ABC book with pages for each letter and have them paste a picture corresponding to the appropriate letter. With an older child, you can have them find characters to make a story from the magazine and find props in catalogs, and then they can write a story based on what they have found. They can even find the setting in a travel magazine or ad.

MIRROR

A mirror is a helpful tool to help a child see what they are doing and learn to manipulate their *own* mouths to fix the error. Talk them through what they need to do so that they know. It's never too early to tell a child they need to put their articulators (tongue, lips, teeth) in a specific position while helping them do it to produce a sound. Eventually, you won't be manipulating their mouth *for* them. They will be learning to do it on their own.

MISTAKES

Let your child know that *mistakes are OK!* We learn from our mistakes. They need to understand that no one is perfect! Adults included! You may need to point out when you make mistakes so they know they are not alone. When you say something incorrectly, **TRY AGAIN**! Mistakes are okay and inevitable when learning new things. The *bigger* lesson is what they do about it. Learning from mistakes and building awareness should be considered a **WIN**!

MOTIVATE

Figure out what motivates your child and use it to your benefit. Use snack time or your child's favorite video to help them **EARN** it. Kids should be *earning* TV or iPad time. You could say that x number of minutes of speech homework earns them x number of minutes on the iPad. You can use snacks to help your child work on articulation. Each kid is different, and each kid will require different motivators. Some will require a 1-1 correspondence of reinforcement during set activities, while others may be able to work for a few minutes before needing a reward/reinforcement.

Don't lose sight of your child's strengths because of their weaknesses. Instead, make use of their strengths to improve their weaknesses. Encourage them and provide rewards to reduce frustration with difficult tasks. A little encouragement goes a long way.

MONKEY

NARRATOR/NARRATE

Think of yourself as a walking narrator. Always talk to your child and help them to understand *what you are doing, why you are doing it,* and *where you are going.* Even if they cannot talk, the fact that you are speaking to them encourages receptive language and vocabulary for them to "understand," which is the key to using that vocabulary expressively.

NEWSPAPER

Use the newspaper to talk about sports and how they are the same and/or different. Ask questions about *what they use to play the game, where they play it, who they are playing, how they play it, etc.* The more involved you are with your child with everyday tasks, the more you expand their vocabulary.

NURSERY RHYMES

Nursery rhymes, songs, and repetitive books like *Brown Bear* help children learn to anticipate words and cue a child to speak. Practice nursery rhymes to assist with anticipating vocabulary, knowing what comes next, and putting words together. Examples include *Jack and Jill, Star Light Star Bright, Twinkle Twinkle Little Star etc.*

After we mix everything together, we will put the dough in the oven and bake it.The cookies will be delicious!

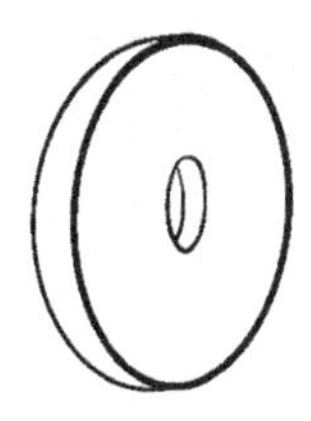

OPEN-DOOR POLICY

Don't hesitate to ask experts questions, such as therapists, doctors, teachers, etc., who are all part of your child's team. We are here to help.

OPPOSITES

Practice opposites to incorporate new vocabulary. If your child isn't sure of the answer, point to it or give clues such as a phonemic clue (first sound of the word). For example, W*here did the balloon go? It didn't go down (point); it went _____ (point UP! or say "uhhh" to clue them into saying "UP"!).*

OTHERS

Use others to assist you. Siblings are helpful assistants. Make sure they understand what is needed to help your child so that they can hold them to the same standard. Many times siblings become the "mini-me" when I leave after therapy. It also significantly helps with carryover. Grandparents and other caregivers need to know your expectations and boundaries for your child, such as nothing is for free. Rather, it is earned.

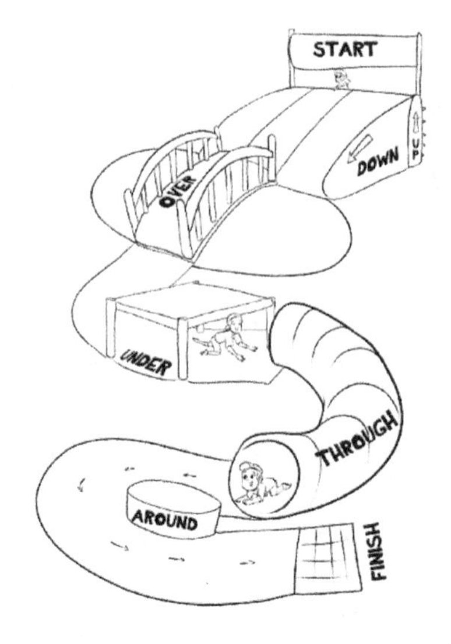

OUTSIDE PLAY

Encourage outdoor play and combine ways they can have fun and learn along the way. For example, create an obstacle course where they must move *up* and *over*, *around* and *through* different things. This encourages following directions, listening, comprehension, vocabulary development, and memory recall.

Play with different balls outside (football, baseball, basketball, beach ball, etc.). Talk about the different things you can do with different balls: *bouncing, catching, throwing, tossing, rolling,* and *kicking.* You can also give them a series of directions for them to follow and then ask questions for understanding. For example, *Throw the ball to Eric and then kick the ball to me. What did Eric do with the ball? Who did he throw it to? Who kicked it? What shape is it? What color is it?*

You can also teach synonyms, antonyms, verbs, etc., using the ball. A *synonym* is a word with the same meaning, big and large or small and little. An *antonym* refers to opposites, like big vs. small.

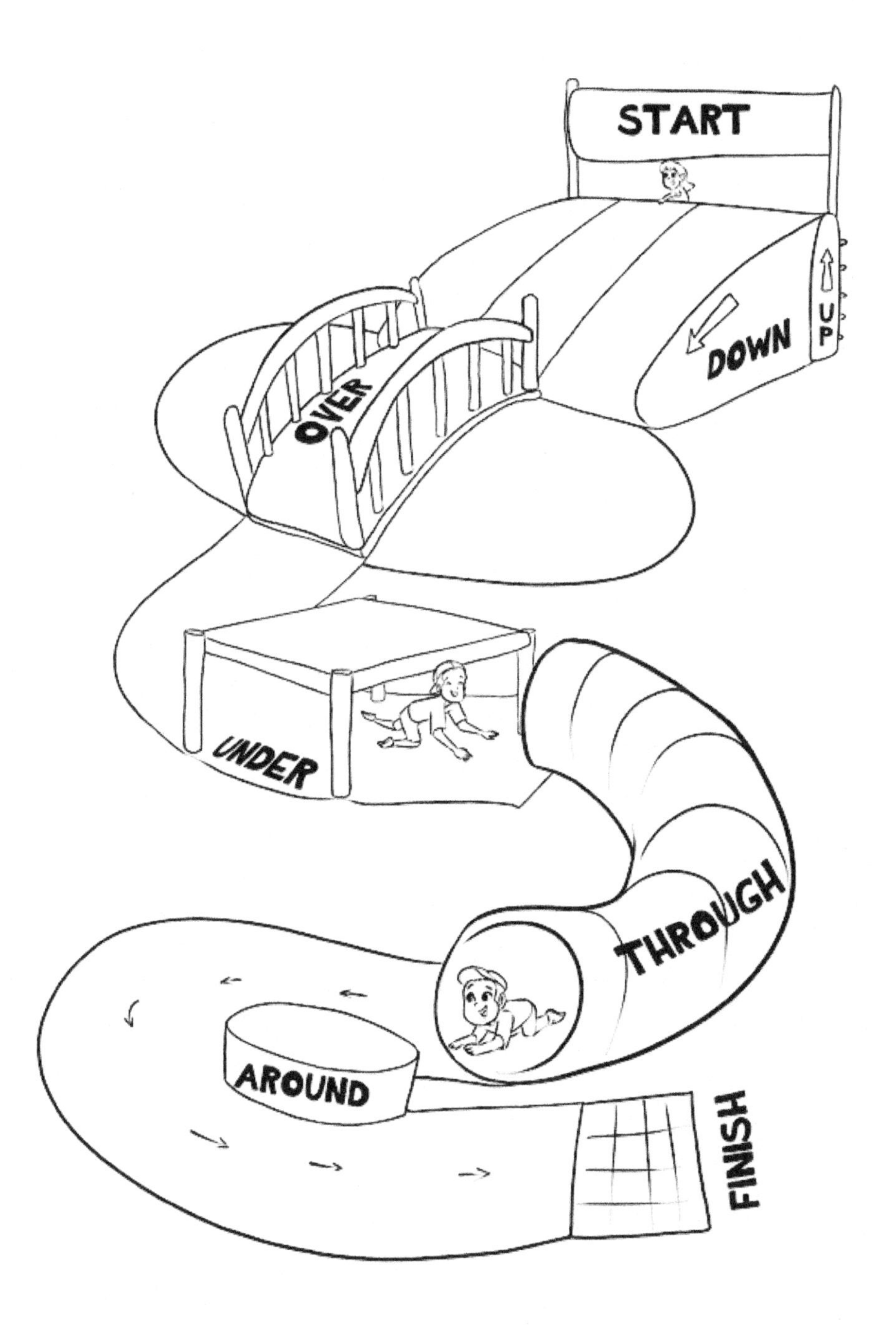
START
UP
DOWN
OVER
UNDER
THROUGH
AROUND
FINISH

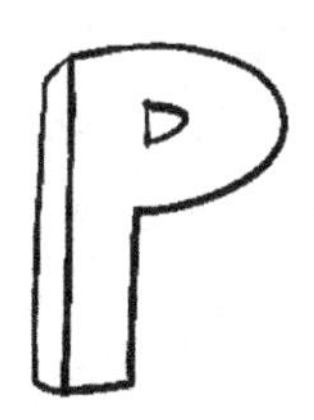

PECS® (*Picture Exchange Communication System*)

This system helps your child interact functionally. It is a vital option if your child is non-verbal and needs a way to communicate. To set up the system, take pictures of what your child plays with, what they eat, and where they go. Print pictures in 3x3 size and laminate them (they don't need to be 4x6). Categorize the pictures such as food, toys, places, etc. Display them on a board on the wall. Your child can take down the appropriate picture and hand it to you in *exchange* for what they want. Your therapist can guide you in using this system creatively.

PENNY JAR

Have a penny jar that you put pennies in when you see your child doing something good, saying their sounds right, or making good choices to do speech HW or whatever it might be. Then, after X number of pennies are earned, they can cash it in. This acts as a visual for them. They should also *lose* pennies if they do not fulfill their requirements. (The rewards need to be age appropriate). *Suggestion: Based on the age of your child, have the rewards they are working for established in advance so they know what they are working for! You could say 10 pennies earns you ___ or 100 pennies earns you ___. You set the criteria. It can be very simple or more elaborate/creative based on your specific child's motivation.*

PICTURES

Find picture scenes of a farm, a house, a zoo, etc. and name animals, objects, people, furniture, etc. that you can put in those places. Ask questions and sing songs related to that place, such as *Old MacDonald* for the farm scene. This song helps children associate animal *noises* with the *names* of animals. It also works on memory since you must remember the order in which you mentioned the animals on the farm as you sing the different verses.

Using family picture albums is an excellent way to *ask questions* about where they live, who lives with them, what their house looks like, what animals they have, what you do when you go over to their house, how you get there, do you fly, drive a car, etc. Your child can also *describe* what people are wearing in the photos.

PLAYTIME

Playtime is critical for learning. Children model what they see. They will use a telephone or cook in the kitchen "just like their mom." Be sure to provide clear examples of how to interact, what language to use, and role play! Make it fun. Have puppet shows, dance parties, or make videos on your smart device. The possibilities are endless.

MR. POTATO HEAD

Using Mr. or Mrs. Potato Head helps a child learn about body parts. The game comes with multiple body parts to choose from, such as different types of eyes, noses, shoes, hats, and more. Talk about what you *do* with your eyes, nose, teeth, mouth, ears, etc. You can also describe the *type of* eyes, nose, or mouth you want to choose—for example, the *blue* eyes, the *red lips*, the *pink* nose, etc.

PRAISE

Be sure to praise your child along the way. Many kids feel that they need to get things right the first time and that, despite trying, it's not good enough. It is imperative to reward attempts, explain that mistakes are part of learning, and let them know that achieving difficult things takes time. Remind them that learning can be hard, but you recognize their hard work.

PRETEND

If you know your child wants something, but they are not using their words to ask for it, pretend to do it. For example, pretend to pour juice into a cup, but do not take the cap off the juice container. Instead, after pretending to pour the juice, give your child the "empty" cup and act normal. The hope is that they will look at the (empty) cup and say/think, "Wait a minute - this isn't right! Where's my juice?" This encourages communication. They have to *TALK* to get what they want.

PRONOUNS

Expanding on photos or Mr. Potato Head ideas, you can incorporate pronouns. Talk about what **HE** (Mr. Potato Head) or **SHE** (Mrs. Potato Head) is doing in the picture. Identify the person's gender (is it a boy or a girl?) first, then decide if we should call them *he* or *she*. Explain that we call boys "he" and girls "she." I see Aunt Susie. *She* is wearing glasses. *She* is wearing pants. I see Cousin Bob. *He* lives in NJ, and *he* has a dog named Fritz.

PUSH

Push your child. Don't let your child give up and look for help every step of the way. Push them to sound out words and figure out answers themselves before giving up or asking for help. Taking that extra time to make *them* do the work and having *them* figure out the answer makes the reward so much sweeter. Building their confidence that they can do it is ideal.

PUZZLES

Use puzzles about people, animals, vehicles, food, places, etc. Ask various questions while working to put the concept of what they are working on together. *Who goes swimming? Where do we go when we are sick? What does a fireman wear on his head? Why do police cars have sirens? When do we eat dinner?* Be sure to include all WH questions (who, what, where, when, why, and how).

When using puzzles, if a child does not know where it goes and you already have a few pieces in the puzzle, give clues to help them find the right spot. For example, the boat goes *next to* the car, or the fish is *above* the tiger. You can also use colors to connect your child to the right spot. Find the *blue* piece.

Ball
Car
Block

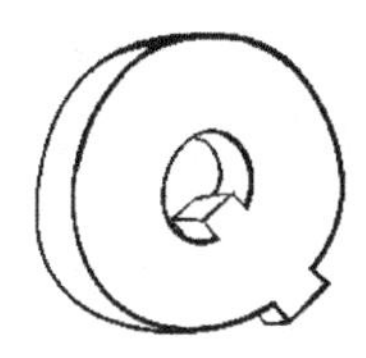

QUIZ/TEST

Always look to see where your child is functioning. Aim high and expect good things and then assess whether you need to break a concept down or adjust as needed. Always ask questions. Kids learn through talking - they are inquisitive by nature.

QUESTIONS

Kids are curious by nature and learn through talking and taking action. Depending on their level, start with open-ended questions and then provide choices if need be. Get your child to think on their own. Use picture stimuli to help with naming.

If you are in the doctor's office or sitting around in a waiting area with your child, show them some pictures on *your phone*. Take advantage of the time you have together. Ask questions about what they think about the experience. For example, *"Remember when we went to the lake with ___? Tell me what you remember. Tell me something fun you did that day."*

When playing a game, have them ask for "more" pieces or to label (expressive language) or point to the pictures (receptive language) for understanding. Ask questions related to the puzzle or game pieces. *Expressive* examples -—> Who rides in a firetruck? What does the fireman drive? "What do they need to put out the fire? *Receptive* Examples —> Show me the fireman—point to what the fireman drives. Ask them: "A truck? That's right! You say "Truck" or /tuh…. rrr….uh….ck/."

Stop and ask questions along the way when reading books or watching movies. Play dumb sometimes and ask questions you already know the answer to in order to give your child the opportunity *to explain it to you.* This also works with music. They don't need to sing every word, but it helps to stop and allow them to catch up with you by pausing and repeating words together.

When your child answers a question with a different type of WH (who, what, where, when, why) response, you should recognize what they said and redirect them to what you were asking. For example, "Yes, this animal *says*, "moo," but I asked what it is *called*. I need to know the name of the animal. We call it a…" (leading phrases help as well). Provide phonemic cueing as necessary to guide them even further.

How was your day?
I met a new friend today.

REAL PROGRESS

Real progress can be seen by engaging in a sing-a-long, whether it's *ABCs* or *Wheels on the Bus*. ABC puzzles are great for learning vocabulary, manipulating pieces, asking for "more," taking turns, following directions, and listening for descriptions to locate a given puzzle piece. Additionally, saying the ABCs allows you to *hear* how your child's articulation is forming.

REVIEW

At the end of the day, have your child summarize the day's events. Talk through it sequentially and ask for details. After asking questions, discuss what they are planning to do the next day or discuss future plans.

REWARD SYSTEM

Build a reward system. You can refer to the Currency section above. Connecting your child's personal currency to action increases your child's success. For example, if a child loves using their iPad, create a connection between earning x number of minutes on their iPad for each minute they put into practicing speech. Other ideas are treats at the dollar store, picking out movies, choosing a special dessert, having mommy and me time, etc. To receive that reward, they must earn a certain number of tickets or points. Some rewards should be quick and easy, while others should require more time to earn.

REINFORCER

An added incentive while working on goals at home can be incorporating bubbles, which are key reinforcers! This typically makes them happy and they will likely say the word(s) or sound(s) correctly to see the bubbles again (*an action causing a reaction).*

Additionally, never accept *I can't* as an answer. Reinforce that learning is hard, but you recognize their hard work. No one is perfect, and everyone makes mistakes, adults included. But you have to *try* to *succeed*. You have to fall down to get back up. As long as they are *trying* and not giving up… that's great!!! The more they try, the better they will get!!!

RHYMING

Rhyming is a great skill to predict a word missing in a poem or to figure out a missing word when used as a cueing technique. Help a child think of the answer "on their own" by offering a clue that it "rhymes with __." That way, they are still figuring out the answer independently, but you are guiding them in the right direction. Example: I'm thinking of something that hops, and it rhymes with RUNNY—it's a (bunny).

What made your day great today?

SEMANTIC ABSURDITIES

Tell your child something silly and have them correct it. They must determine what is wrong with what you said and know how to correct it. For example, you put a hat on your elbow. *That's not right*—you put a hat on your *head*!

SCAVENGER HUNT

If your child struggles to connect letters and letter sounds, go on a scavenger hunt for objects. Give them a letter, practice the sound, and then send them around the house looking for things that start with that sound. For example, if the letter was B, you would practice saying "buh buh buh" and then ask them to find things in the house with the /b/ sound. For some kids, you may need to limit the space they look at as the "whole house" may be too overwhelming. For example, bathtub, bathroom, broom, basket, biscuit, brush, ball, bubbles, etc.

SIRI (an Apple virtual assistant)

Surprisingly Siri, which can be used on the iPhone or iPad, is helpful for practicing articulation. Since you must speak clearly into the phone to be understood, it can help with pronunciation. I have had some families tell me that their child's speech had remarkedly improved as a result of talking to SIRI since they needed to enunciate their words clearly to be understood!

SONGS AND SINGING

Songs are a fun way for kids to learn how to talk. They can sing along, fill in the blank, or use finger-play to sing (hand gestures like *Itsy Bitsy Spider* or *Wheels on the Bus).* Another idea is to sing the alphabet. Listen for the correct pronunciation of each letter. If a letter sound is incorrect, pay attention and address that sound through imitation and labeling of pictures. A few other song suggestions are *Row Row Row Your Boat, 5 Little Ducks, Head, Shoulders, Knees, and Toes,* and *Old MacDonald Had a Farm,* to name a few. Pause singing if they need time to catch up. Don't rush it. When you sing a song, leave out a few words and have your child fill them in. This way, they can anticipate what is coming.

SIGN LANGUAGE

Sign language *elicits* communication. It does not hinder it. A fun way to learn signs with your child can be through https://www.signingtime.com/. This is a fun and interactive way to learn basic words. When you're teaching basic signs to kids, be sure to pair the sign with the word (verbally). Eventually, you will *withdraw* the sign and *encourage the vocalization* on its own. Another suggestion to learn keywords is at: (https://www.handspeak.com/word/).

Learn a few key and purposeful signs (more, please, help, hurt, drink, eat, all done, etc.) for basic communication but pair with a verbalization to help them understand that the *purpose* is to talk with our mouths.

SPATIAL

If you are working on spatial concepts *(in, on, under, next to, in front of, behind, etc.),* you can make a game of it, such as *Simon Says.* Tell them, "Simon says, 'Stand behind the chair.' Simon says, 'Put your foot under the chair.'" Be patient and wait for them to physically respond to the verbal cues you are giving them.

STORIES

You can create stories using objects or magnetic objects. These are not *just* for **GROUPING** and **SORTING** items that **GO TOGETHER** but can help a child use their imagination to create a sentence. An older child can take this one step further and WRITE the sentence on paper.

For example, using the objects of girl, fish, and net, you can create the sentence—*The girl went fishing and caught one in the net!* Girl/bike—*The girl rode her bike to school.* Different combinations with the girl can include a girl with a bike, X-ray, umbrella, quilt, hat, juice, etc.

STRUCTURE

Say what you mean. Kids need structure. If you have a set of expectations, such as they have more chances before they get **XYZ**, you need to follow through. Teach your children that what you say holds weight and that they do not have endless opportunities. They have to earn their way out if they go into a timeout. Example: If they went in timeout for crying and not talking, they should be given a chance to talk and say things to get out of a timeout. First and foremost, they have to be calm in order to earn their way out of timeout.

SYLLABLES

If a child has difficulty saying words, you can *tap the syllables* and/or words on the table or their arm. You can try using hand-over-hand assistance if your child doesn't understand what to do initially. Take their hand and say a sentence aloud. Then, with each syllable and/or word, tap the table, their arm or even clap! You can use bean bags for each word unit of the sentence by laying out three to four bean bags (you can use anything instead of a bean bag) to start and say a sentence such as "I am big." For each word, tap a new bean bag. You can decide which way would be easier based on the age and/or level your child is functioning at. **HINT**: If they are deleting sounds to words, breaking it down by syllables might be easier. However, if they are omitting certain words in a sentence, then it would be more appropriate to tap the words.

All done!

TAKING TURNS

Turn-taking is important for kids to learn for obvious reasons. They need to learn that a conversation is two-sided and that you ask questions and wait for answers that provide information. Many goals of communication require interaction. If you interrupt and ignore what the other person is saying, it becomes difficult to communicate and understand the other person. Make good eye contact and follow social cues.

Several games promote taking turns and social interaction, such as *Candy Land.* Let them know everyone has their turn and must wait for their next turn. You may allow your child to help *you* with *your* turn (giving them more practice without realizing it), and then when it's *their* turn, they can do it independently.

Turn-taking is key. Don't always let your child be the winner or do things *their* way or on *their* terms. Instead, help them learn that everyone gets a turn and they must wait their turn. They still learn by being part of the process, even when it's someone else's turn.

TV OR OTHER SCREEN TIME

If you allow a certain amount of TV a day or week, talk to your child after the show is over. Better yet, watch the show *with* your child and ask questions during the commercials. *What do you think will happen next? Where do you think they are going? Who is that in the blue shirt? Where do they live?*

TAPPING

When a child has difficulty saying certain words, tapping on their hand, arm, shoulder, or leg helps them understand the "parts" of a word. For example, when saying a word like "potato," which has three syllables, tap on their arm as you say "puh…tay…toe" to help them hear the three parts. Usually, they will tap back, which is good, so they will understand they need to say three syllables. Using your fingers as visuals works as well.

TIME

Talking about "before and after" helps with the concept of time and the sequencing of events. *What did we do before breakfast? What did we do after we went to the pool? What do you need to do before you go to bed?*

Dedicate time every day to work on your goals. Set aside structured time while also working on goals and weaknesses throughout the day while out and about (in the car, at bathtime, at the grocery store, driving to/from school, etc.).

What are the cars doing?

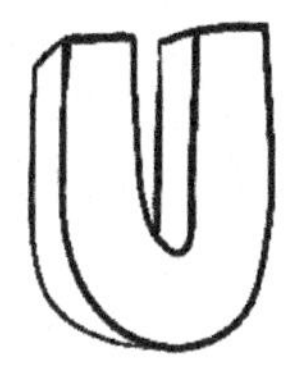

UNDERSTAND

Understand that your child has difficulty learning and you are there to help. Giving help is not cheating or doing it for them as long as you encourage them to talk, repeat, follow your model, etc. If your child doesn't know "how" to interact, you are simply giving them the tools to know how to do it so that when they are on their own, they will know what to do because you have taught them.

Understand the importance of follow-through. If you don't follow through on what you say, you are teaching your child that your words don't have meaning. Be strong and don't give in, or you will teach them that when you say "no," they can still get what they want.

UNO - Play the game of **UNO** and take out the **ACTION** and **WILD** cards. This is a simple, yet fun, way of working on **COLOR** and **NUMBER** matching.

I'm going to ask you one more time to clean up. If you don't, you'll go in timeout.

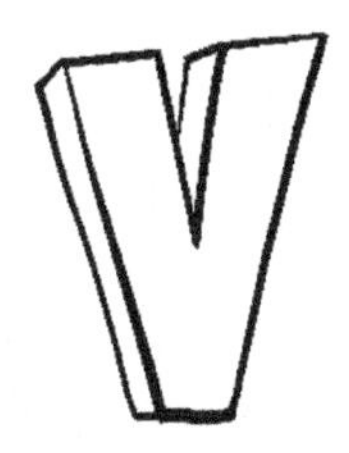

VIDEO

Use video to reflect on where you are now and how far you have come. Taking video is a great record keeper for you to see the progress that might not be obvious due to everyday interactions. Sometimes it takes stepping back and realizing where your child was when you started your journey to discover where they are now and to relish their progress.

Look at the situation from a half-full perspective. There is always something to learn; as long as you provide those opportunities, your child will continue to mature, develop, and effectively communicate with those around them.

Using video and pictures helps your child see what a great job they are doing. Many times kids will talk repeatedly when they see themselves on video. It reinforces the skill/word etc. They want to see themselves, so seize the opportunity. Take videos of others doing something you want your child to learn to do (wave/say hi or bye) so that by watching the video of a familiar face, they may engage and connect with it more.

VISUALS

Use a picture chart to help your child understand what to expect on a given day. If your child cannot read, seeing the sequence of their day in pictures, is an added benefit.

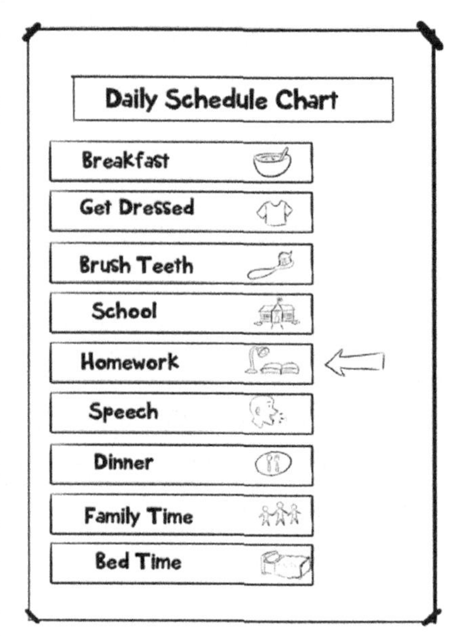

This will help with understanding what comes first, next, after that etc.

If your child wants to watch TV, they can see on the chart where that will occur. Thus, they will understand "First homework, then _____" or "First speech, then TV time" to know that TV comes after ____."

VOCABULARY CARDS

If you have vocabulary cards, have your child group the pictures together by *similarities*. Then you can also discuss ways they are *different*. For example, if you are talking about animals, find all the 4-legged ones. Then identify how they are different. For example, some may be big/heavy, while others are short and don't have a tail. You can keep breaking the piles into smaller groups until you get to two VERY similar animals.

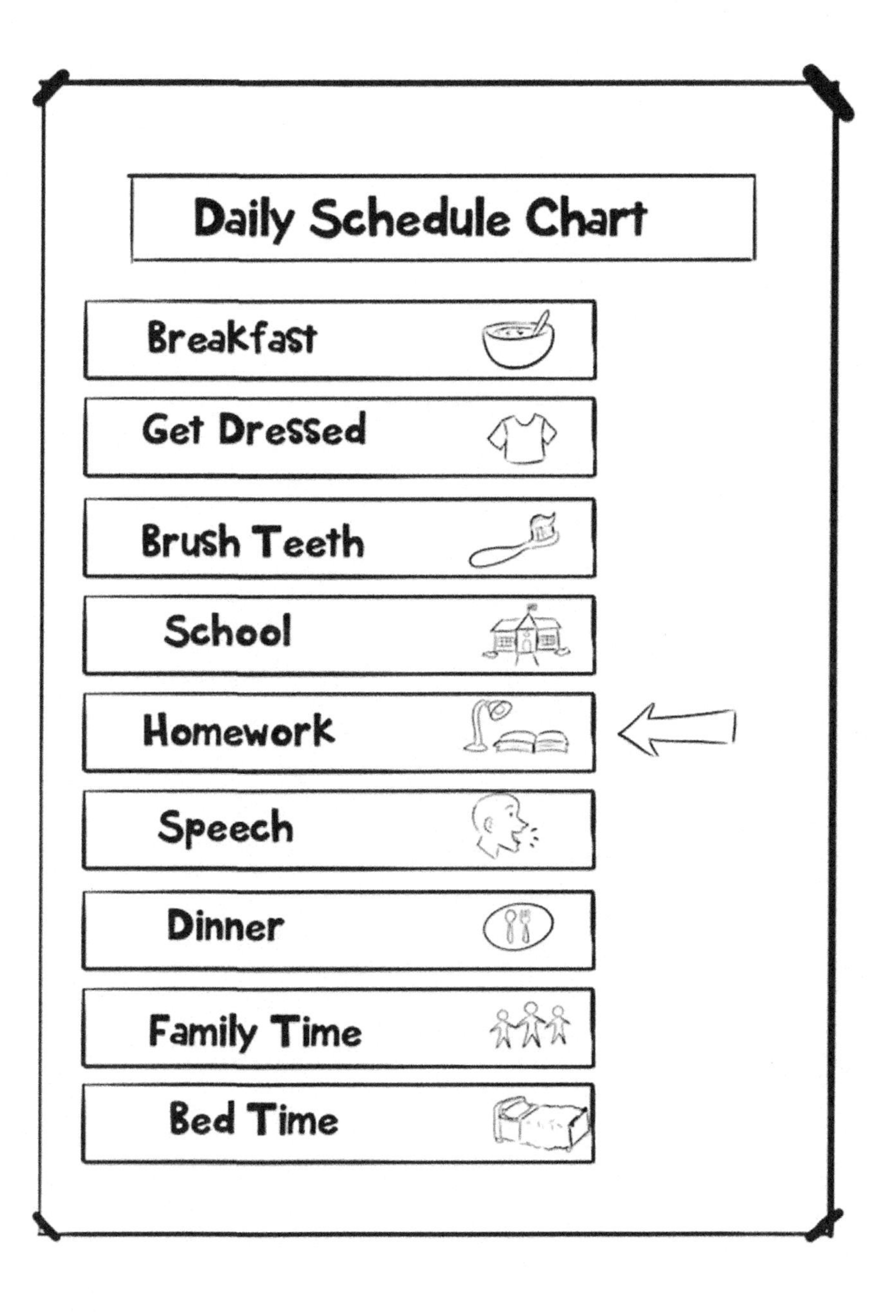
Daily Schedule Chart
Breakfast
Get Dressed
Brush Teeth
School
Homework
Speech
Dinner
Family Time
Bed Time

WELCOME

Welcome new ideas to keep things fresh. Find blogs, listen to podcasts, use Google searches, read articles, visit websites, and use social media to be creative. This helps you grow and can point you in the right direction. Be bold and pose a question on social media, such as in a Facebook group, to see who else might have experienced or had the same inquiry.

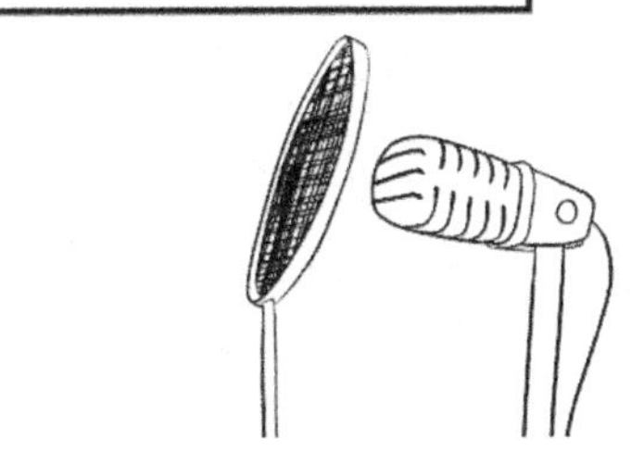

The *Be Kind to Everyone* podcast is a great resource to help those connected to people with or without autism. It is broadcast by a family who has a daughter with autism where they discuss how they got to where they are today - while spreading kindness and making the world a kinder place for individuals with disabilities.

https://podcasts.apple.com/us/podcast/be-kind-to-everyone/id1620394642

WANTS AND NEEDS

Encourage your child to say, "I need help," when they don't know the answer. Give examples of the proper way to express what they want and need. For example, "I want to go to the pool!" or "I want to play with my friends at the park!" This will encourage children to express their thoughts and feelings even when they don't know the answer.

Talk about the things necessary to complete an activity. For example, ask them what they need to do when they are dirty, hungry, sleepy, or upset. *For example, What do you need to bring with you when you go to the pool?* (towel, sunscreen, pool toys).

Be Kind
to everyone

EXAMINE your strategies. Repetition is good, but variety is also the spice of life. Be sure to repeat, repeat, and repeat, as repetition and bombardment are crucial to learning. But, at the same time, balance it with variety and occasionally approach a goal from an unexpected angle.

EXAMINE yourself. Are you giving things away for free? Are you making it easy on yourself by handing things over and not requiring your child to talk? Think about the end goal. Do you want your child to rely on you every step of the way or do you want your child to be an independent thinker? Your actions and choices impact that end goal.

What can I do to help?

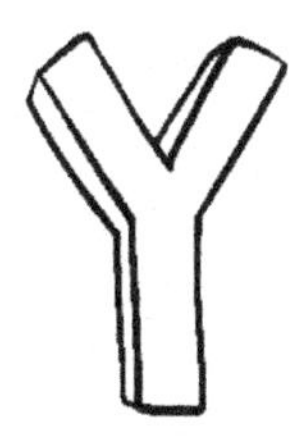

You can do it! Don't give up. Your child will improve quicker the more you incorporate goals and require things of them. Doing it ***for*** them only sets them back. Giving in will make it harder each subsequent time you try to say "no." The quickest way from point A to point B is if you do it for your child, but your child isn't benefiting from other people doing things for them. *Slow down, take your time, take breaks,* and *talk*. This will help you and your child work through the complicated processes they encounter. The more time you take now, the less time you will need to help them in the future.

YOU have two choices

Give your child two choices with behavior or two choices with answering a WH question (Who, What, When, Where, Why). It's not black and white—it's not clear-cut. But you and your child have two choices in handling things. Talk them through it by reminding them of the choices - if they do "this," then they get "that" - or if they *do not do this,* then they *do not get that*. Keep it simple.

You have two choices.
Stop splashing or
Get out of the pool!!!

ZOO AND OTHER FIELD TRIPS.

Use different themes to help you work on questions and ideas related to the topic/location, etc. Pick a different theme each week or each month and work crafts, snacks, and other activities around those themes. Work together to find answers to questions you don't know the answers to. Take a nature walk and talk about what is around you, labeling things. Make connections to objects and help your child see things around them as connected and intertwined rather than isolated parts.

EXAGGERATE your responses! **EMPHASIZE** what you want to say. **Be animated**! The more fun and energetic you are, the more tuned in your kids will be!

Way to go!
Woah! That's fast!

FINAL THOUGHTS...

- ☑ Praise progress and success. Don't always focus on what they are NOT doing— focus on what they are doing RIGHT, so they are encouraged to do MORE of it.
- ☑ You have to MAKE a change to SEE a difference. "Insanity" is defined as doing the same things over and over again yet expecting different results.
- ☑ Remember, kids are sponges ready to learn at the drop of a hat. Act like a narrator in their life and always talk to and include them in everything you do. The more you share, the more they will absorb and learn. Each lesson can be taught repeatedly or differently each time. Your involvement is the key to helping them practice their skills and carryover what they have learned in therapy and/or school to each new day.
- ☑ Thanks for playing such an active role in your child's life. They will not disappoint you!
- ☑ I promise they will thank you for the time you spent with them in these very early stages of their learning.

What People Are Saying About ASTS

After 3 years of speech classes twice a week at school, our 10-year-old twin boys were showing no signs of correcting their lisps.

We found Robyn through our insurance, and in 9 months she taught our kids what the public schools couldn't do in 3 years.

She is very professional, organized, and takes into account all the details of not just teaching speech, but also schedules.

She would meet with our kids at our house, grandparents' house, a library, our school, etc. to make sure they would always get their lessons consistently.

Admittedly, it took us 2-3 months to grasp the importance of our role to make sure our kids practiced each day. Robyn was great at helping us learn how to help our kids practice their speech routinely. She helped us come up with games and reward systems to motivate our kids to practice and self-correct their speech.

Robyn demands the best from her students and their parents because she really cares about them and wants them to succeed. She is honest when they are progressing and honest when she thinks they are not doing their best or regressing.

She was kind enough to never complain that our new dog was constantly interrupting their speech sessions because he wanted her to pet him, even though I'm sure he was driving her crazy!

If you're looking for a speech therapist to do all the work for you and tell you everything is sunshine & roses, then you should look elsewhere. But if you want someone who will get your children the results you want - whatever their speech challenges may be - there is no one I would recommend more.

Our kids quickly took to Robyn and loved their speech sessions, this told us they truly liked and trusted her.

Thank you, Robyn!
Matthew, Dad

My daughter has been taking speech with Miss Robyn at Advantage Speech Therapy Services for a few months. I can definitely see a transformation in her speech and annunciation. Robyn is so friendly, patient, smart, and kind with my daughter. I also appreciate the Fusion app for scheduling, which allows me to see the notes from each session and work with my daughter at home on the items practiced that day in session. I would totally recommend Advantage Speech Therapy Services to everyone. The best part is they're able to come to my daughter's school, give her the lesson, and then she's right back in class learning, all while I'm able to stay at work and not have to attend or bring her to the sessions. Tele-therapy is also available if needed. Robyn also sends videos of some sessions to me. I love being able to see my baby learning and practicing her words! I would give Advantage Speech Therapy Services a 10 out of 10 and will definitely refer everyone I know who is looking. Thank you!!

Brianna, Mom

Robyn at Advantage Speech Therapy Services was exceptional in helping our 5-year-old son. He was struggling with pronouncing the letter "R." We had initially thought we would wait to see if he would outgrow his speech impediment, but it began to affect his self-esteem negatively. Robyn made the process so convenient by coming to his school to work with him. Our son actually looked forward to his sessions because he enjoyed the time with Robyn! We saw a significant improvement in his R's in just a few short months. Robyn uses up-to-date methods for therapy, which leads to great success for your child. I highly recommend Advantage Speech Therapy to anyone with a child struggling with any speech issue. Thank you, Robyn, for taking such a great interest in our son!

Sam, Dad

Robyn has been a God send for my granddaughter! Robyn immediately made her feel comfortable and safe, and, as a result, my granddaughter has made amazing progress in a very short period of time. In previous therapy situations, Emma has not responded to the therapist, but

Robyn's warmth, engaging activities, and encouragement have made a tremendous impact on her. Robyn has given her the confidence that she needs to be able to succeed. We will forever be grateful!

Paula, Grandma

As an SLP, I've had the privilege of being mentored by and working with Robyn for two years. She is a truly gifted speech pathologist. She's dedicated her career to helping kids improve their communication skills and find their voices. Robyn is not just a skilled professional; she is a kind and compassionate soul who deeply cares about her clients and is quick to celebrate their progress.

Overall, I cannot recommend Advantage Speech enough. Robyn and her team are truly dedicated to helping kiddos improve. If you're looking for compassionate care, expert skills, and a warm and welcoming environment, then Advantage Speech is the place for your child.

Rachel H, Pediatric SLP

Our experience with Robyn has been top-notch from the beginning, and we highly recommend her to our friends who are having the same challenges. We are so grateful for Robyn's help (and patience!). She is very responsive, always keeps me up to date on our son's progress, and helps him through speech issues he's had for years. We are incredibly proud of the work our son puts in, and Robyn's ability to hone in on what he needs is such a blessing.

Dayna, Mom

My kid's been seeing Ms. Robyn for almost a year now, and we couldn't be happier! He's using many more words and complete sentences. Even his confidence increased!! I particularly love the tips she gives after the sessions on what to work on with your kid at home. It's helped my family tremendously!

Renata, Mom

The best speech therapy you can ever find. Ever since my son started with them, he has gotten so much better. I recommend them 100%!

Perla, Mom

At 18 months, our daughter was non-verbal -- no words, no Mama or Dada, not even babbling. She just sat and stared into space, rarely making eye contact. Within six months, Robyn had engaged her, pulled her out of her shell, and gotten her to make sounds and speak several hundred words. Over the next two years, Robyn gave our daughter the tools to interact with the world -- not just to speak.

By kindergarten, she had so few remaining symptoms the teacher was astonished she'd ever been labeled ASD. Now, my miracle Eva is in 5th grade. She's talkative, social, artistic, empathetic, and, above all, confident! I could never have wished for a better therapist than Robyn. Our family will be forever grateful!

Peggy, Mom

Made in the USA
Columbia, SC
03 July 2023

19986585R00075